THE DEFINITIVE AUDITION SONGBOOK FOR MEN

18.95

CONTENTS **DISC ONE**

CONTENTS **DISC TWO**

© 2010 by Faber Music Ltd
First published by Faber Music Ltd in 2010
Bloomsbury House 74–77 Great Russell Street
London WC1B 3DA
Edited by Lucy Holliday
Photo ©Paul Mitchell/Redferns Music Picture Library

ISBN10: 0-571-53233-0
EAN13: 978-0-571-53233-9

Printed in England by Caligraving Ltd

The text paper used in this publication is a virgin fibre
product that is manufactured in the UK to ISO 14001
standards. The wood fibre used is only sourced from
managed forests using sustainable forestry principles.
This paper is 100% recyclable

To buy Faber Music publications or to find out about the
full range of titles available, please contact your local music
retailer or Faber Music sales enquiries:

Faber Music Ltd, Burnt Mill, Elizabeth Way,
Harlow, CM20 2HX England
Tel: +44(0)1279 82 89 82
Fax: +44(0)1279 82 89 83
sales@fabermusic.com fabermusic.com

AMAZED

Words and Music by Chris Lindsey, Marv Green and Aimee Mayo

CD1 track 1

1. Ev-'ry time our eyes meet, this feel-ing in-side me is al-most more than I can
2. The smell of your skin, the taste of your kiss, the way you whis-per in the

CD1 track 2

ANGELS

Words and Music by Robert Williams and Guy Chambers

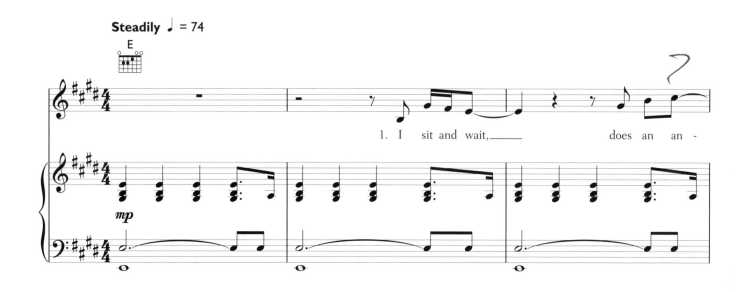

1. I sit and wait,_____ does an an -

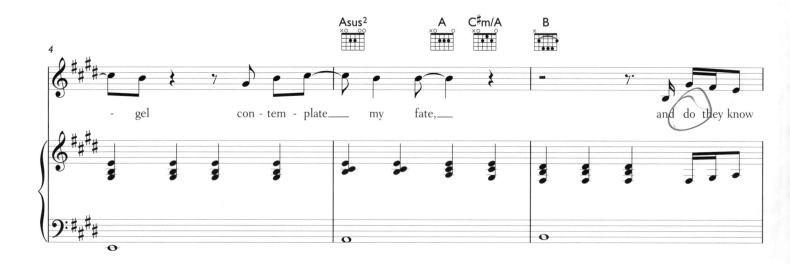

- gel con - tem - plate_____ my fate,_____ and do they know

the pla - ces where we go when we're grey and old?_____

And through it all＿ she of‐fers me＿ pro‐tec ‐ tion, a lot of love and af‐fec‐

CD1 track 3

ARE YOU GONNA GO MY WAY

Words and Music by Lenny Kravitz and Craig Ross

CD1 track 4

BRIGHT EYES

Words and Music by Mike Batt

CAN'T TAKE MY EYES OFF YOU

Words and Music by Bob Crewe and Bob Gaudio

CD1 track 6

CRAZY

Words and Music by Thomas Callaway, Brian Burton,
Gianfranco Reverberi and Gian Piero Reverberi

FLY ME TO THE MOON

Words and Music by Bart Howard

CD1 track 7

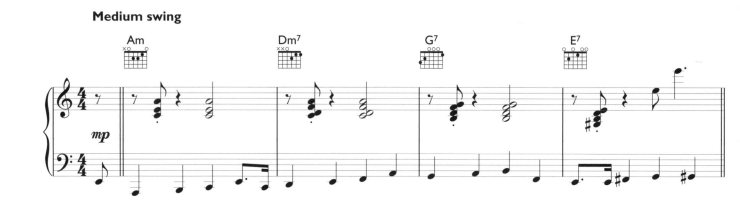

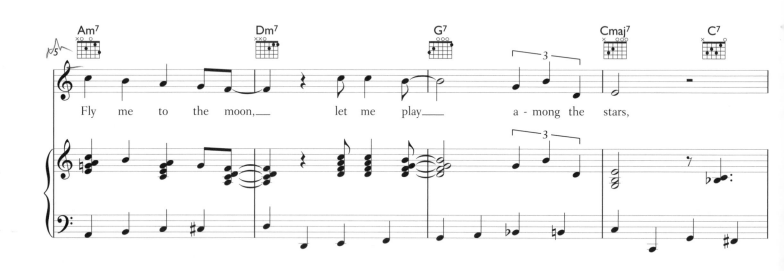

Fly me to the moon,___ let me play___ a - mong the stars,

let me see what spring is like on a - Ju - pi - ter and Mars. In

GREASE

Words and Music by Barry Gibb

1. I solve my prob-lems and I see the light, we got a lov-in' thing, we got-ta feed it right.

There ain't no dan-ger we can go too far,___ we start be-liev-in' now that we can

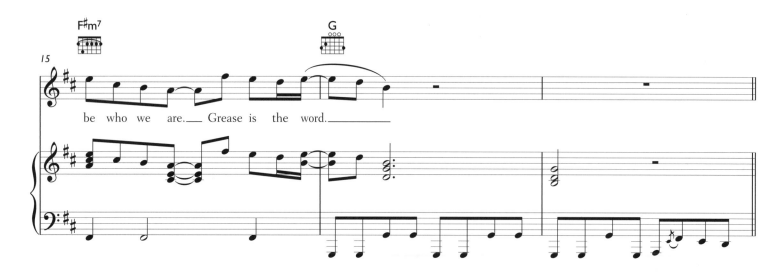

be who we are.___ Grease is the word._____

2. They think our love is just a grow - in' pain, why don't they un - der - stand_ it's just a
3,4. We take the pres - sure and we throw a - way con - ven - tion - al - i - ty___ be - longs to

cry - in' shame?_____
yes - ter - day._____

Their lips are ly - ing on - ly real is real,___ we stop the
There is a chance that we can make it so far,___ we start be -

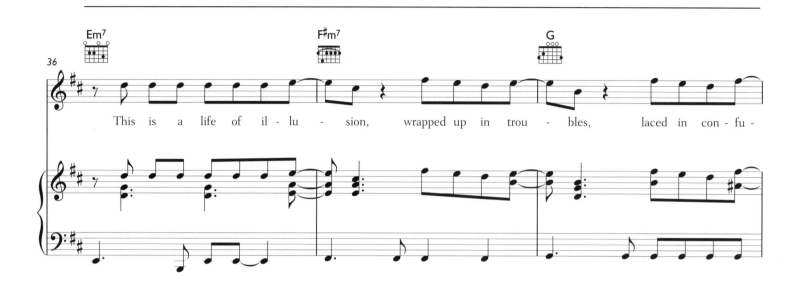

This is a life of il - lu - sion, wrapped up in trou - bles, laced in con - fu -

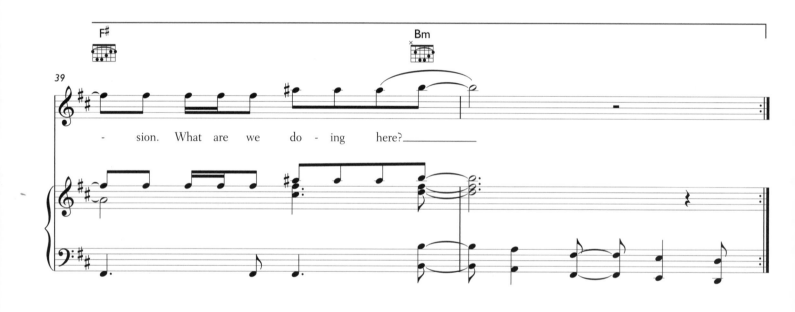

- sion. What are we do - ing here?

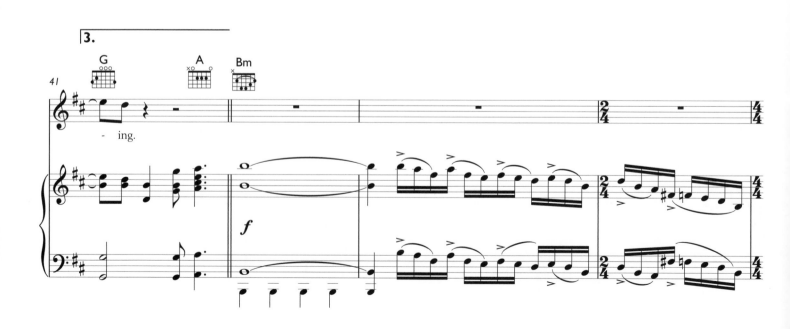

3.

- ing.

CD1 track 9

GREASED LIGHTNIN'

Words and Music by Jim Jacobs and Warren Casey

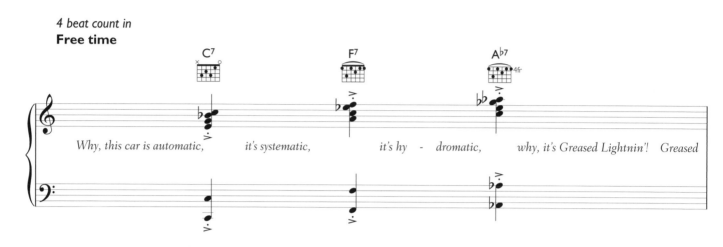

CD1 track 10

HALLELUJAH, I LOVE HER SO

Words and Music by Ray Charles

1. Let me tell you 'bout a girl I know, she is my ba-by and she

CD1 track 11

HANDBAGS AND GLADRAGS

Words and Music by Mike D'Abo

58

CD1 track 12

HAVE YOU MET MISS JONES?

Words by Lorenz Hart
Music by Richard Rodgers

HERO

Words and Music by Enrique Iglesias, Paul Barry and Mark Taylor

CD1 track 13

Spoken: Let me be your hero...

1. Would you dance if I asked you to dance?

Would you run and nev-er look

CD1 track 14

I BET YOU LOOK GOOD
ON THE DANCEFLOOR

Words and Music by Alex Turner

♩ = 205   **Fast Rock**

Just bang-ing tunes in D - J sets and dirt-y dance - floors

____ and dreams of naugh - ti - ness.

CD1 track 15

I'LL BE THERE FOR YOU

Words and Music by Michael Skloff, David Crane,
Phil Solem, Marta Kauffman, Allee Willis and Danny Wilde

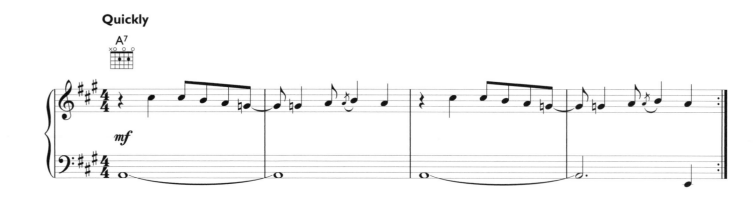

1. So, no - one told___ you life___ was gon - na be___ this way,___
2. You're still___ in bed___ at ten___ and work be - gan___ at eight.___

your job's___ a joke,___ you're broke,___ your love life's D. O. A.___
You've burned___ your break - fast, so far, things are go - ing great.___

IT'S NOT UNUSUAL

Words and Music by Gordon Mills and Les Reed

CD2 track [1]

1. It's not un-u - su-al___ to be loved by a-ny-one.___
2. It's not un-u - su-al___ to go out at a-ny-time.___
3. It's not un-u - su-al___ to be mad with a-ny-one.___

(2° & 3° only)

It's not un-u - su-al___ to have fun with a-ny-one.___
But when I see___ you out___ and a - bout it's such a crime.___
It's not un-u - su-al___ to be sad with a-ny-one.___

But when I   see____   you   hang   -   ing   a - bout____
If   you   should   ev   -   er   wan   -   na   be   loved_
But   if   I   ev   -   er   find___   that   you've   changed

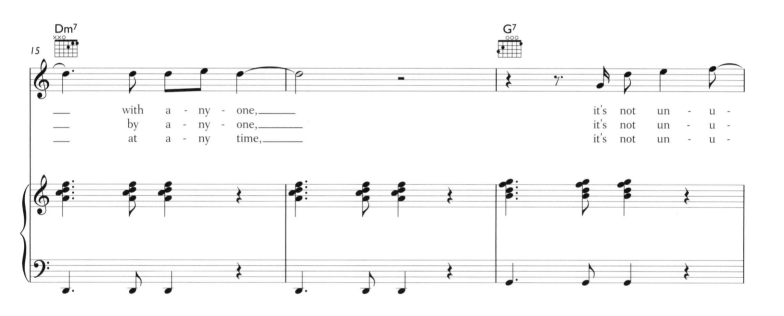

with   a   -   ny   -   one,_____   it's   not   un   -   u   -
by   a   -   ny   -   one,_____   it's   not   un   -   u   -
at   a   -   ny   time,_____   it's   not   un   -   u   -

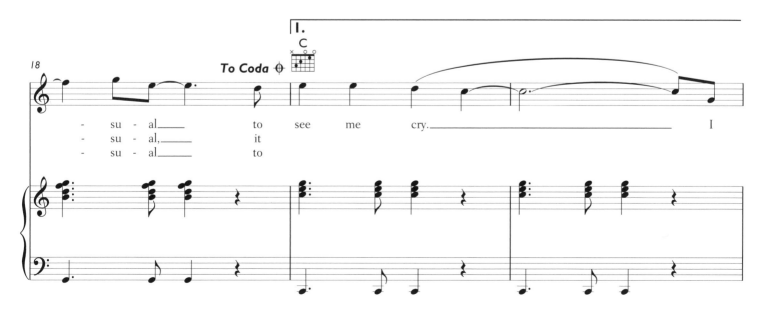

-   su   -   al____   to   see   me   cry._____   I
-   su   -   al,____   it
-   su   -   al____   to

CD2 track 2

JESUS TO A CHILD

Words and Music by George Michael

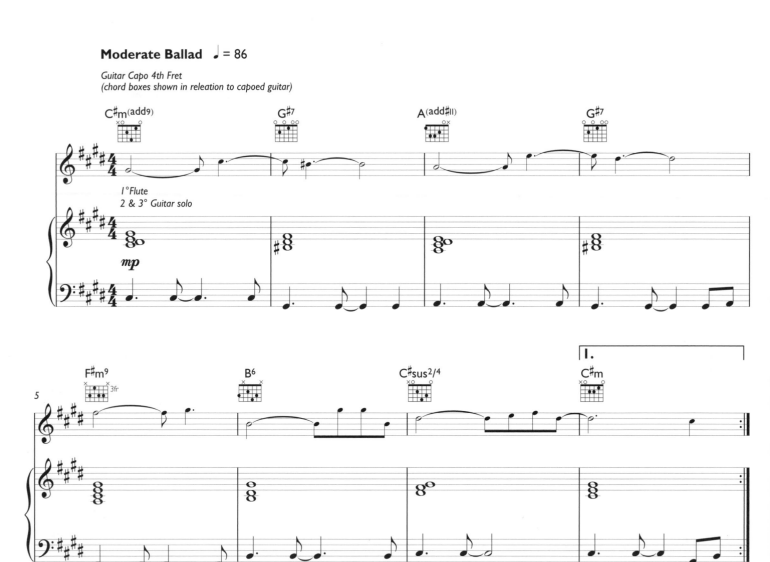

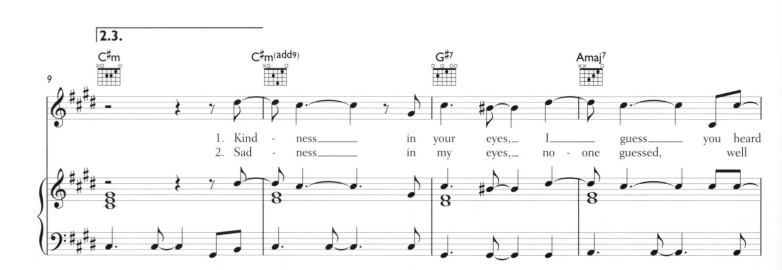

1. Kind - ness in your eyes, I guess you heard
2. Sad - ness in my eyes, no - one guessed, well

CD2 track 3

LET THERE BE LOVE

Words by Ian Grant
Music by Lionel Rand

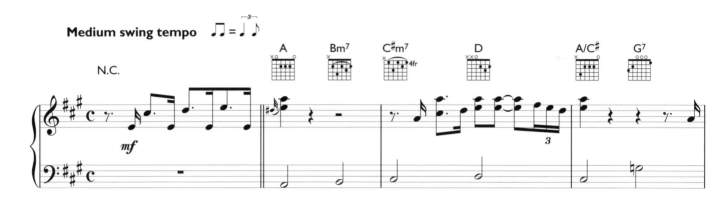

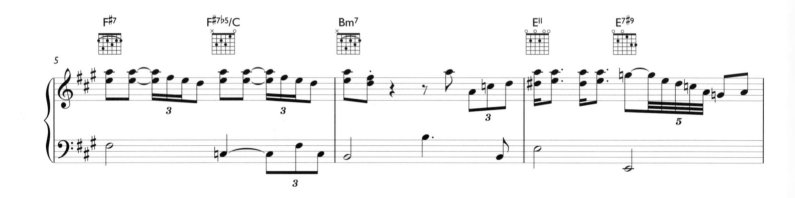

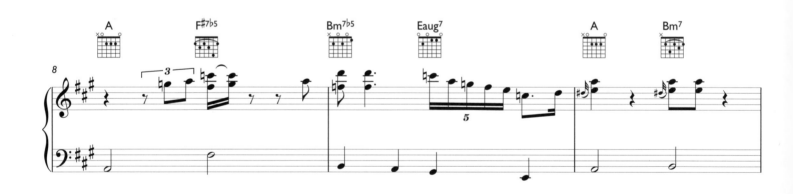

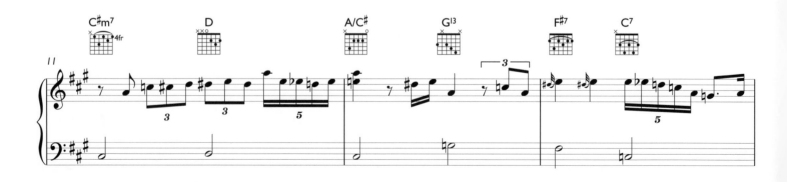

LET'S STAY TOGETHER

Words and Music by Al Jackson Jr, Al Green and Willie Mitchell

MAKE ME SMILE
(COME UP AND SEE ME)

Words and Music by Steve Harley

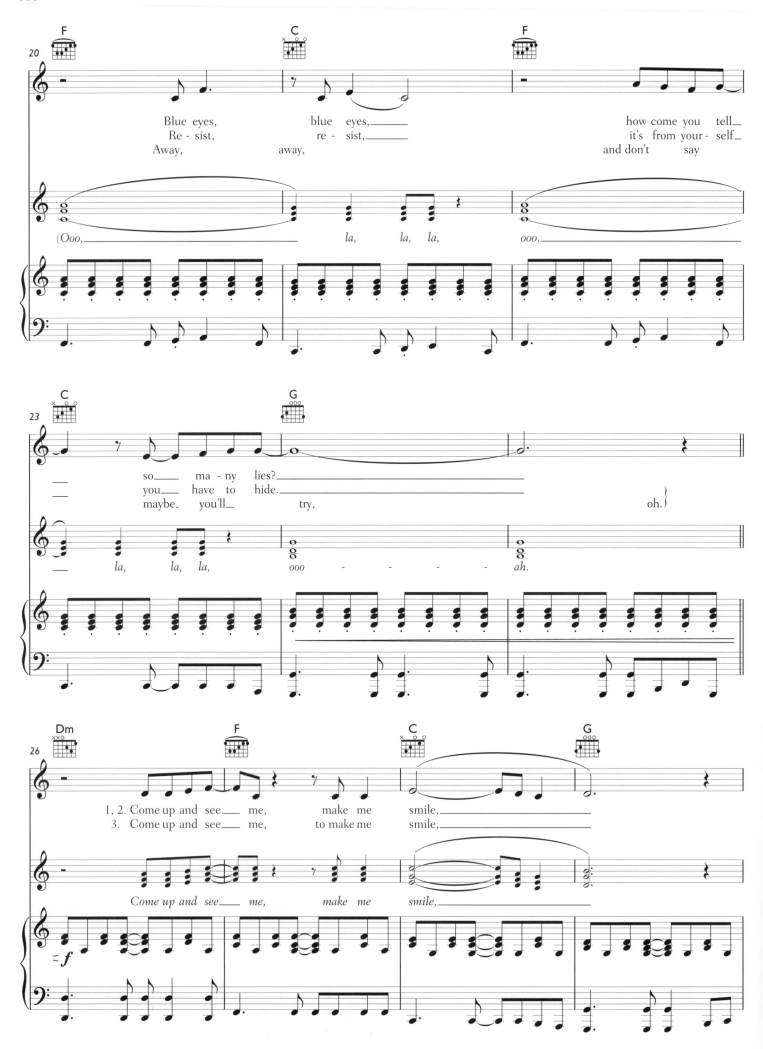

CD2 track 6

ME AND MRS JONES

Words and Music by Kenneth Gamble, Cary Gilbert and Leon Huff

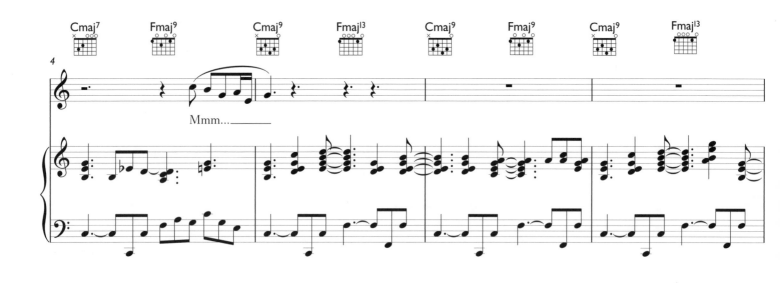

Mmm...

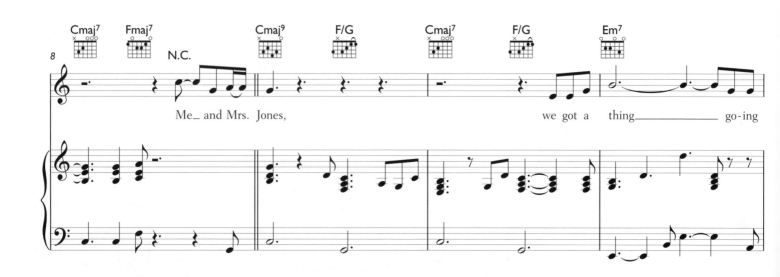

Me_ and Mrs. Jones,   we got a   thing_____ go-ing

CD2 track 7

MR. BOJANGLES

Words and Music by Jerry Jeff Walker

2.

E♭aug   B♭aug/D   Cm⁷   B♭   B♭⁷/D

dance,   and dance,   and dance,_____ please_____ dance._____

E♭   B♭/D   Cm⁷   B♭/D   F⁷/C   B♭⁷/D

Come back and dance a - gain Mis - ter Bo - jan - gles._____

E♭   B♭/D   Cm⁷   B♭   F⁷/C   B♭⁷/D

Whistle

E♭   B♭/D   Cm⁷   B♭   F⁷/C   B♭⁷/D   E♭

CD2 track 8

MAGGIE MAY

Words and Music by Rod Stewart and Martin Quittenton

1. Wake up, Mag - gie, I think I got some-thing to say to you,___
(Verses 2-4. see block lyrics)

it's late Sep - tem - ber and I real - ly should_ be back_

118

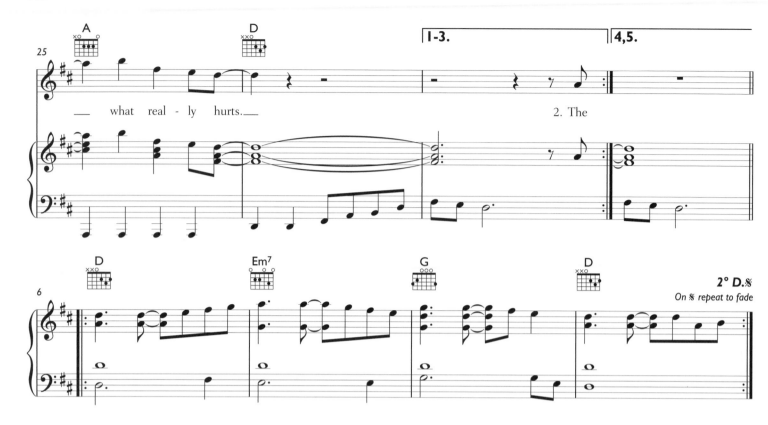

_ what real - ly hurts._

2. The

2° D.%
On % repeat to fade

Verse 2:

A
The morning sun, when it's in your face G
D Really shows your age
A But that don't worry me none G
D In my eyes, you're everything
G I laughed at all of your jokes D
G My love you didn't need to coax A - F#m
Em Oh, Maggie, I couldn't have tried any more Em Asus4
Em You led me away from home A
Em Just to save you from being alone A
Em You stole my soul, and that's a pain I can do without. D
Em

Verse 3:

All I needed was a friend
To lend a guiding hand
But you turned into a lover, and, mother, what a lover!
You wore me out
All you did was wreck my bed
And, in the morning, kick me in the head
Oh, Maggie, I couldn't have tried anymore
You led me away from home
'Cause you didn't want to be alone
You stole my heart. I couldn't leave you if I tried.

Verse 4:

I suppose I could collect my books
And get on back to school
Or steal my daddy's cue
And make a living out of playing pool
Or find myself a rock 'n' roll band
That needs a helping hand
Oh, Maggie, I wish I'd never seen your face
You made a first-class fool out of me
But I'm as blind as a fool can be
You stole my heart, but I love you anyway.

CD2 track 9

THE ONE I LOVE

Words and Music by Michael Mills,
William Berry, Peter Buck and Michael Stipe

♩ = 126

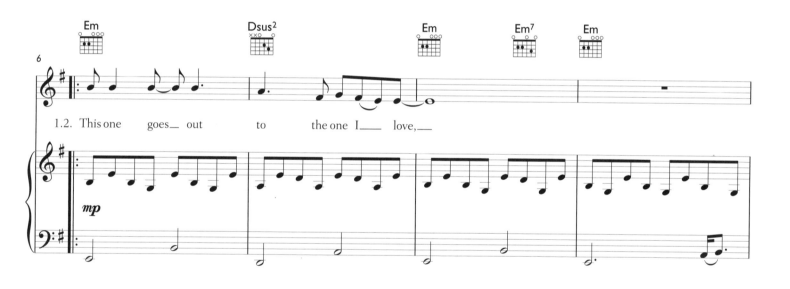

1.2. This one goes_ out to the one I_ love,_

this one goes_ out to the one_ I left be-hind._

120

SHINE

Words and Music by Gary Barlow, Jason Orange,
Howard Donald, Mark Owen and Steve Robson

CD2 track 11

VOLARE

Music by Domenico Modugno
Original Words by Francesco Migliacci Jr
English Words by Mitchell Parish

Vo- la - re, _____ oh, oh! _____ Can-
- la - re, _____ oh, oh! _____ Can-

-ta - re, _____ oh, oh, oh, oh! _____ Let's
-ta - re, _____ oh, oh, oh, oh! _____ Nel

fly way up to the clouds, a - way from the mad - den - ing crowds; We can
blu, di - pin - to di blu, fe - li - ce di sta - re las sù. E vo-

CD2 track 12

WAKE ME UP WHEN SEPTEMBER ENDS

Words and Music by Billie Joe Armstrong, Michael Pritchard and Frank E. Wright III

wake me up___ when Sep- tem - ber ends.___

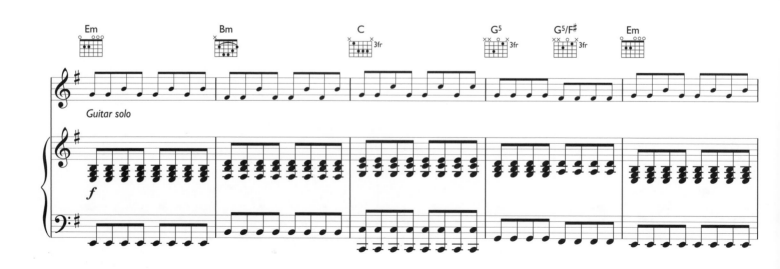

Guitar solo

YOU RAISE ME UP

Words and Music by Rolf Lovland and Brendan Graham

140

moun - tains, you raise___ me up___ to walk on stor - my___ seas. I am

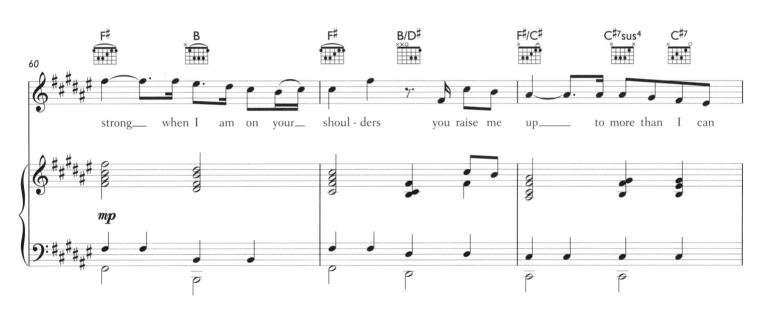

strong___ when I am on your___ shoul - ders you raise me up___ to more than I can

Much slower

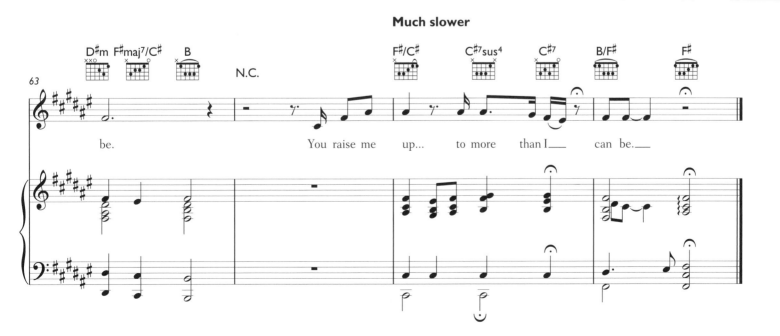

be. You raise me up... to more than I___ can be.___

YOU'RE BEAUTIFUL

Words and Music by James Blunt, Sacha Skarbek and Amanda Ghost

CD2 track 15

YOU SEXY THING

Words and Music by Errol Brown